HOOT

by
Carl Hiaasen

Student Packet

Written by
Veda Boyd Jones

Edited by
Lyn M. Pfordresher

Contains masters for:
- 3 Prereading Activities
- 1 Study Guide
- 11 Vocabulary Activities
- 6 Literary Analysis Activities
- 1 Writing Activity
- 2 Comprehension Quizzes
- 1 Novel Test

PLUS Detailed Answer Key

Note

The Borzoi Book hardcover edition of the book, published by Alfred A. Knopf, © 2002, was used to prepare this guide. The page references may differ in other editions.

Please note: This novel deals with sensitive, mature issues. Parts may contain profanity and or/descriptions of violence. Please assess the appropriateness of this book for the age level and maturity of your students prior to reading and discussing it with them.

ISBN 1-58130-811-6

To order, contact your local school supply store, or—

Novel Units, Inc.
P.O. Box 97
Bulverde, TX 78163-0097

Web site: www.educyberstor.com

Name ______________________________

Clue Search

Directions: Collect information about the book for each of the items. Write down the information and then make some predictions about the book.

Information Source	Information Provided
Dedication	
Title	
Cover Illustration	
Teasers on the cover	
Friends' recommendations	
Reviewers' recommendations/awards won	

Your predictions about the book:

Name ________________________________

Directions: Use an atlas to respond to the following.

1. Find Montana on the United States map. What borders it?

2. What bodies of water border Florida?

3. What type of climate does Florida have? (Look at the equator.)

4. What is the capital of Florida?

5. Locate the Everglades National Park in Florida and Yellowstone National Park in southern Montana and northern Wyoming.

6. Locate the towns of Naples, Florida, and Bozeman, Montana.

Name ________________________________

Directions: Think about the ideas listed below and freewrite for about five minutes on each of the ideas. Be prepared to discuss your thoughts with other students. Finally, write your predictions about the novel on the lines provided.

1. endangered species

2. bullies

3. friendship

4. policemen

5. dysfunctional family

6. humor

7. owls

Predictions: ____

____

____

____

____

Name ______________________________

Directions: Write a brief answer to each study question as you read the novel at home or in class. Use the questions to guide your reading and prepare for class discussion.

Chapter One, pp. 1–12

1. What school does Roy attend?
2. Who is the bully on the bus?
3. Who does Roy see running?
4. What is going to be built at the surveyed site?
5. Who does the policeman think tore out the stakes?
6. What does the policeman trip over?
7. Who does Roy's father work for?
8. Who does Roy talk to at lunch?
9. What does Roy's new friend invite him to do?
10. Who does Roy think the running boy might be?

Chapter Two, pp. 13–23

1. Who is Dana tormenting on the bus when the chapter opens?
2. What does Roy do to Dana on the bus?
3. What happens to Roy on the golf course?
4. Where was Roy born?
5. What did Roy do the night he learned his family would be moving to Florida?
6. Why did Roy want to stay in Montana?
7. What is Roy's punishment for fighting on the bus?
8. What does Miss Hennepin see on Roy's neck?
9. What does Miss Hennepin tell Roy to do?

Chapter Three, pp. 24–36

1. What happened at the building site for the second time?
2. What reason does Roy give his parents for getting off the bus?
3. What medical treatment does Roy receive for the bump on his head?
4. For whom does Roy think his father works?
5. What's on the poster in Roy's room?
6. Which word does Roy misspell in his apology letter?

Name ________________________________

7. How big was the largest alligator in the toilet?
8. Who does Officer Delinko believe has vandalized the building site?
9. Why does the policeman want to be on the Mother Paula patrol?

Chapter Four, pp. 37–48

1. Where is Dana on Monday?
2. What does Garrett think will happen the next time Dana sees Roy?
3. What is the name of the curly-haired girl?
4. What movement does Officer Delinko see at the construction site?
5. What happens to the policeman's car?
6. What does Roy tell Beatrice after she seemed angry on the bus?
7. What is Beatrice's reaction when Roy speaks forcefully to her?
8. Where does Mrs. Eberhardt take Roy?
9. What does Roy give Dana?

Chapter Five, pp. 49–57

1. Why won't the school punish Dana?
2. What does Roy find at the low end of the thicket?
3. What is on the tails of the snakes?
4. How did Roy learn to stand so still?
5. What happens to Roy after he sees the snakes?
6. What do some people call the boy who owns the snakes?
7. Where does the boy let go of Roy?

Chapter Six, pp. 58–70

1. What does Roy's father read in the newspaper?
2. Why does the address sound familiar to Roy?
3. Why did the chief say the policeman was taking flu medicine?
4. What is Officer Delinko's punishment?
5. On what do the kids make bets?
6. What does Curly say will be at the job site next time?

Name ______________________________

7. What does Roy find at the campsite?
8. Who takes Roy's bike?

Chapter Seven, pp. 71–84

1. Where does Beatrice take Roy?
2. What does the truck smell like?
3. What is in the shoebox?
4. How are Beatrice and the barefoot boy related?
5. How does Officer Delinko hear of the missing boy?
6. Why does Beatrice call her stepbrother Mullet Fingers?
7. How does Beatrice flatten the bike tire?
8. What does Officer Delinko ask Roy to do?
9. What does Officer Delinko do when Roy's mother asks if he knows the policeman whose windows were painted?

Chapter Eight, pp. 85–97

1. Why can't the tire be repaired?
2. Why is Roy's suspension from the school bus lifted early?
3. Who is angry with Curly because of construction delays?
4. What does Curly do to stop the vandalism?
5. How many and what type of dogs does Curly bring?
6. What type of bird does Roy see in Florida that also lives in Montana?
7. What happened to Dana's lip?
8. What does Roy ask Dana to do?
9. Who sits next to Dana?

Chapter Nine, pp. 98–110

1. Who warns Roy about the planned attack by Dana?
2. What happened to Roy's mother when he was four?
3. Who does Roy walk with after school?
4. How is Roy saved from the attack?
5. What happens to the dogs at the job site?

Name ________________________________

6. What does the dog handler threaten?
7. What happens to the dog handler's ankle?
8. How does Curly get inside the job shack?
9. How many snakes does the snake wrangler find?
10. Where does Dana take Roy?
11. Who rescues Roy?

Chapter Ten, pp. 111–124

1. What does Beatrice do to Dana?
2. Where does Beatrice take Roy?
3. What kind of favor does Beatrice need from Roy?
4. What does Beatrice tell Roy's mom they are doing?
5. What does Beatrice get from Roy's mom?
6. What will Beatrice's stepmother do if she knows her son is in town?
7. Who is injured?
8. What is the injury?
9. Where do Roy, Beatrice, and Mullet Fingers take the hamburger?
10. Why can't the snakes bite?
11. What do Roy, Beatrice, and Mullet Fingers do with the hamburger?

Chapter Eleven, pp. 125–138

1. What does Officer Delinko find at the construction site?
2. Who is Beatrice now carrying on the bike?
3. What happened to Mullet Fingers as he was climbing over the fence?
4. After the chase, where does Roy find Beatrice and Mullet Fingers?
5. What weapon does Curly take with him to the site?
6. What does Curly shoot?
7. What does Officer Delinko put in his trunk?
8. What does Officer Delinko want Roy's father to do?
9. Where is Roy's mother going?

Name ______________________________

Chapter Twelve, pp. 139–152

1. How do Roy and Beatrice get Mullet Fingers to the hospital?
2. Why does Roy give his name to the hospital clerk?
3. Where does Beatrice say the dog attack occurred?
4. Why doesn't the doctor believe the story?
5. Why does Beatrice leave the hospital?
6. Why won't Beatrice tell Roy the boy's real name?
7. Why does Roy leave the emergency room area?
8. Who brings Roy's parents to the hospital?
9. Who do Roy's parents find in the hospital bed?
10. What does Roy tell the doctor about Mullet Fingers?

Chapter Thirteen, pp. 153–162

1. What book does Roy show his father?
2. What does Roy not tell his father?
3. What did Roy and his father see while on a float trip?
4. What does Roy's father decide to do about the running boy?
5. How did Mullet Fingers get out of the hospital?
6. What did Mullet Fingers leave on the policeman's car antenna?
7. What must Roy balance to make a decision about the owls?

Chapter Fourteen, pp. 163–179

1. Who calls Roy to find out about Dana being tied to the flagpole?
2. Where is the first place Roy rides after his bike is fixed?
3. Why can't Beatrice come out?
4. Where is the second place Roy rides?
5. Why does Dana's father think Roy is there?
6. What does Roy hope to accomplish at Dana's?
7. Where is the third place Roy rides?
8. Where does Mullet Fingers take him?
9. What does Mullet Fingers catch?
10. What does Mullet Fingers say will happen that night?

Name ______________________________

Chapter Fifteen, pp. 180–196

1. What does Roy do outside of Dana's window?
2. Why does Roy intentionally slow down?
3. How does Roy get Dana to promise not to fight anymore?
4. Why doesn't Curly have his pickup?
5. What happens to Dana's feet?
6. What name does Dana call himself when Curly asks?
7. Who captures Dana?
8. Where does the policeman take Dana and Curly?
9. What two things does Dana request?

Chapter Sixteen, pp. 197–210

1. Who tells Roy about Dana's arrest?
2. What do the boys think will happen to Dana?
3. What has Curly left at the site?
4. What vandalism does Curly discover when he returns to the site?
5. Where does Curly find his gun?
6. Where do the Eberhardts go on Sunday afternoon?
7. How many alligators does Roy see?
8. Why does Roy feel a kinship with Mullet Fingers?
9. What does Roy hear when he's in bed?

Chapter Seventeen, pp. 211–228

1. When will the groundbreaking event occur at Mother Paula's?
2. If someone sees an owl, what two animals does Chuck Muckle tell Curly to say they are?
3. What did the rattraps do to Dana?
4. What does her teammate say has happened to Beatrice?
5. Does Officer Delinko think Dana is the vandal?
6. What duty is Officer Delinko assigned?
7. What does Officer Delinko give Dana?

Name ______________________________

8. How late in the year have owls been known to have fledglings?
9. Where is the city hall file on permits and inspection notices?
10. What does Roy take to the site?
11. Who does Roy talk to about the owls?

Chapter Eighteen, pp. 229–248

1. Why doesn't Curly tell the policeman about the missing seats?
2. What does Officer Delinko find in the burrow?
3. How tall is the baby owl?
4. What does Roy see in the newspaper?
5. How did Beatrice break her tooth?
6. Who did Beatrice's father talk to in the garage?
7. Why is Roy called to the vice principal's office?
8. What does Roy take to Mullet Fingers?
9. What current event does Roy present to his class?
10. What does Roy tell the class he will do the day after he announces his current event?

Chapter Nineteen, pp. 249–258

1. Who signs Roy's permit to leave school at noon?
2. On what is Beatrice's note written?
3. What does Beatrice give Roy?
4. Who is in the stretch limo?
5. What does Kimberly Lou Dixon mistake for roaches?

Chapter Twenty, pp. 259–274

1. Who shows up at the site to support Roy and Beatrice?
2. Who is most surprised when Roy speaks up?
3. Who carries signs about the owls?
4. Who covers the event for the media?
5. Where is Mullet Fingers?
6. What is in the bucket?

7. What does Chuck Muckle do to the snakes?
8. What is Chuck Muckle going to do to Mullet Fingers?
9. Who joins the ring of students in front of Mullet Fingers?
10. Who arrives to talk to Mullet Fingers?

Chapter Twenty-one, pp. 275–281

1. What is Mullet Fingers' real name?
2. What is on the front page of the newspaper?
3. What did Chuck Muckle do to a reporter?
4. Who is at the door?
5. Why is the file Roy gives the reporter important?

Epilogue, pp. 282–292

1. Who did the pancake house executives bribe?
2. Who will Kimberly Lou Dixon star with in a movie?
3. What job does Chuck Muckle take when he leaves the pancake house?
4. How much money does the pancake house give to the Nature Conservancy?
5. Why does Mullet Fingers choose to escape with Dana?
6. Where does Roy go to find Mullet Fingers? What does Roy do there?
7. Who puts the fish in Roy's sneaker?

Name ______________________________

incredibly (3)	dispatcher (4)	monetary (5)	malicious (7)
cackled (10)	clammy (10)	skeptical (12)	rasped (14)
doggedly (16)	perpetually (18)	unprovoked (18)	consternation (20)
inedible (21)	encountered (22)	confronted (22)	snidely (22)
balefully (23)	reproachfully (23)		

Directions: Match each definition below to the correct word from the vocabulary list above.

1. ___________________: like a hen's cry
2. ___________________: can't be eaten
3. ___________________: constantly
4. ___________________: with determination
5. ___________________: relating to money
6. ___________________: moist, sticky, and cool
7. ___________________: one who transmits information by radio to police patrols
8. ___________________: doubtful
9. ___________________: a state of dismay
10. ___________________: not roused into action

Name ______________________________

vandalism (24)	leniency (28)	assault (28)	wrangler (34)
disgruntled (35)	surveillance (40)	intrigued (40)	hunch (40)
mused (41)	involuntary (43)	decisive (43)	formidable (44)
forthrightly (44)	disintegrated (45)		

Directions: Write each vocabulary word in the left-hand column of the chart. Complete the chart by placing a check mark in the column that best describes your familiarity with each word. Working with a partner, find and read the line where each word appears in the story. Find the meaning of each word in the dictionary. Together with your partner, choose ten of the words checked in the last column. On a separate sheet of paper, use each of those words in a sentence.

Vocabulary Word	I Can Define	I Have Seen/Heard	New Word For Me

Name ______________________________

errant (49)	impenetrable (50)	gingerly (52)	glade (53)
lumbered (53)	perpetrators (62)	disciplinary (63)	terminated (64)
inevitable (65)	altercation (66)	ominously (68)	kiosk (69)

Directions: Choose three words from the vocabulary list. Turn to the page on which each is used in the text. After examining how the words are used in context, complete the word map.

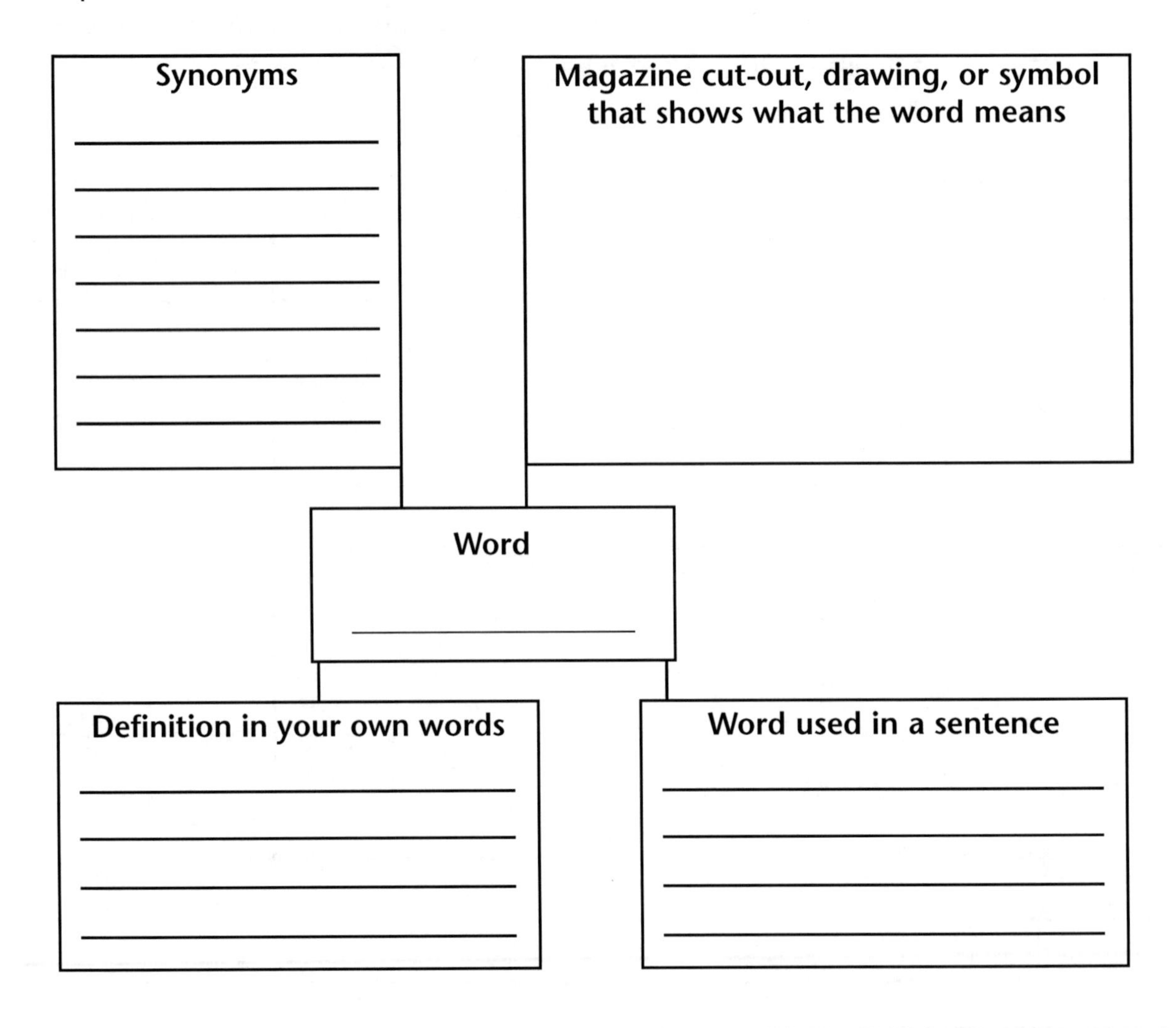

Name ______________________________

fervidly (77)	mulling (77)	defiant (77)	persistent (77)
squall (78)	scudded (78)	wolverine (81)	informant (82)
noncommittal (83)	incentive (85)	acknowledged (86)	franchise (87)
gala (89)	ferociously (91)	fledgling (93)	disconcerting (94)
nonchalantly (96)	oblivious (96)		

Directions: Read each word below. The first letter of a related vocabulary word appears after each word. The related word may be either a synonym or an antonym. Write the related vocabulary word on the line and circle the words that are antonyms.

1. resistant—d______________________________
2. certain—n______________________________
3. storm—s______________________________
4. indifferently—n______________________________
5. fiercely—f______________________________
6. quitting—p______________________________
7. admitted—a______________________________
8. unenthusiastically—f______________________________
9. aware—o______________________________
10. motive—i______________________________
11. celebration—g______________________________
12. ignoring—m______________________________

Name ______________________________

stupendous (98)	remorse (100)	groveling (100)	mottled (105)
snidely (107)	peevish (107)	pungently (108)	girded (109)
manic (111)	appraising (118)		

Directions: Write each vocabulary word from the list above in the center column of the chart. Write an antonym for the word in the left-hand column and a synonym for it in the right-hand column.

Antonym	Vocabulary Word	Synonym

Name ______________________________

fugitive (128)	sullenly (129)	subterranean (130)	contemplate (131)
avail (132)	skulking (132)	accusations (135)	tandem (150)

Directions: Replace each underlined word(s) with one word from the vocabulary list. Then write a sentence using one of the vocabulary words.

1. She pushed and pushed on the heavy safe, but to no benefit; it would not budge.
2. The three boys lifted the lid in a group effort.
3. He stared at the painting and found the girl's beauty something to think about.
4. She saw him lurking around the warehouse.
5. The lion was an escapee from the exotic animal park.
6. His charges against the man were based on facts, not just hearsay.
7. She gloomily glanced at her mother, who was making her eat the broccoli.
8. The underground fort was a wonderful hiding place.

Sentence: ____

____

____

____

____

Name ______________________________

particulars (153)	interrogating (153)	obligated (155)	cowls (156)
sheepishly (157)	truancy (158)	turbulence (158)	physique (164)
materialized (165)	poised (165)	apprehension (173)	reconnaissance (174)
reluctance (175)	crusade (175)	surge (175)	dilapidated (176)
ravages (176)	sanctuary (176)	exerting (178)	

Directions: Select ten vocabulary words from the list above. Create a crossword puzzle answer key by filling in the grid below. Be sure to number the squares for each word. Blacken any spaces not used by the letters. Then, write clues to the crossword puzzle. Number the clues to match the numbers in the squares. The teacher will give each student a blank grid. Make a blank copy of your crossword puzzle for other students to answer. Exchange your clues with someone else and solve the blank puzzle s/he gives you. Check the completed puzzles with the answer keys.

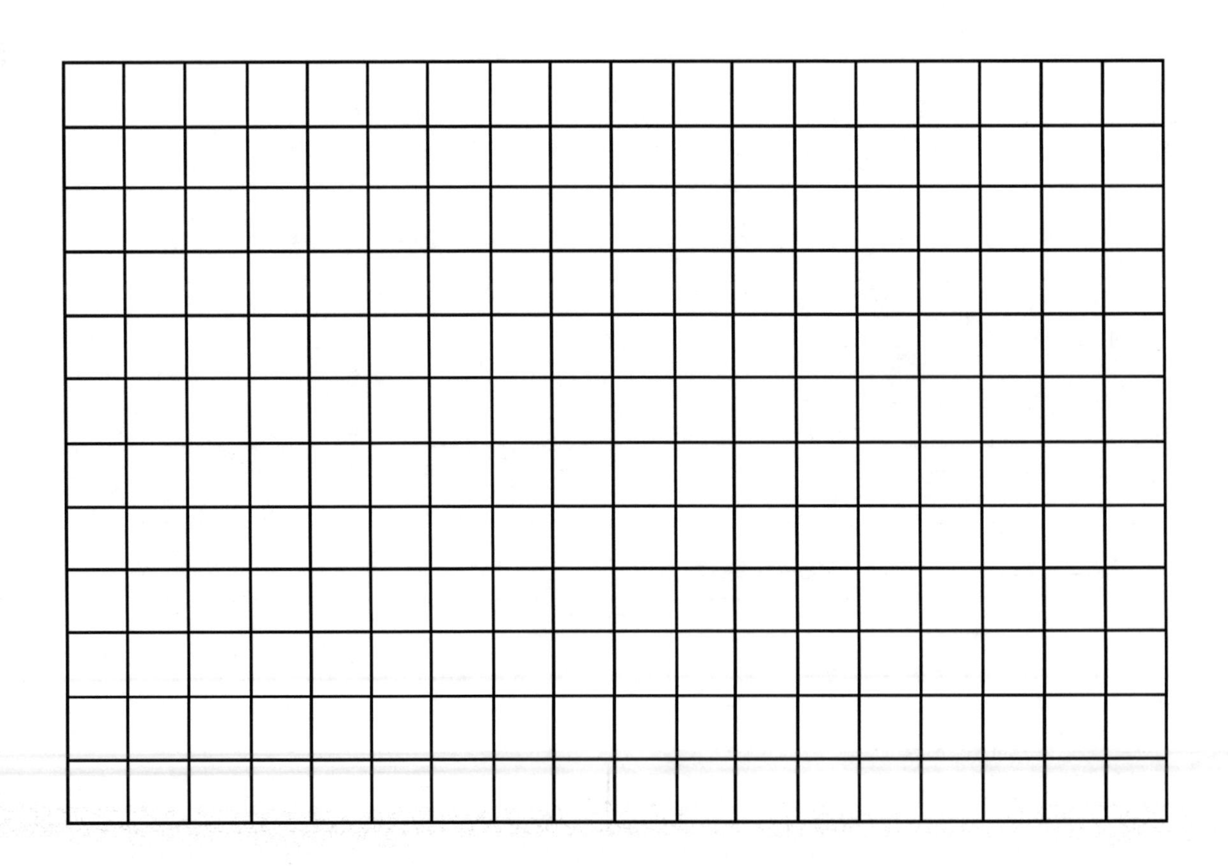

Name ______________________________

malevolently (184)	patronizing (185)	yarn (186)	fiasco (188)
morphed (189)	florid (194)	liberation (199)	methodical (202)
harrowing (202)	feverishly (203)	accomplice (203)	sabotaged (203)
wretchedly (204)	interjected (207)		

Directions: Write each vocabulary word in the correct column below.

Noun	Verb	Adjective	Adverb

Name ______________________________

version (211)	rankled (214)	tormentor (215)	bungled (215)
phenomenal (216)	apprehended (219)	tauntingly (219)	brawny (222)
amber (232)	frenzied (232)	pilfered (237)	incisor (238)
jurisdiction (240)	gaunt (241)	skeptically (243)	defiantly (243)
agitated (246)	allegations (247)		

Directions: Use the vocabulary words above to answer the following questions.

1. If you have a yellowish stone, what color could be used to describe it?
2. What might a dentist fill?
3. If a boy is very thin, how would you describe him?
4. If someone is extremely excited about something, they are what?
5. A judge cannot hold court in an area where he has no what?
6. If a man is undernourished, he is certainly not what?
7. If a boy steals a candy bar, he has done what?
8. What is another name for a bully?
9. If a criminal is caught, he has been what?
10. If someone makes formal charges against someone, he has made what?

Name ______________________________

improbable (250)	discreet (254)	exasperation (254)	dubiously (256)
commotion (260)	dignitaries (262)	miffed (262)	slanderous (263)
inconsiderate (265)	pivoted (271)	tranquil (272)	

Directions: Choose eight vocabulary words from the list above. Write the words on the numbered lines below.

1. ______________________________ 2. ______________________________
3. ______________________________ 4. ______________________________
5. ______________________________ 6. ______________________________
7. ______________________________ 8. ______________________________

On a separate sheet of paper, use each of the following sets of words in an original sentence. Your sentences should show that you know the meanings of the vocabulary words as they are used in the story.

Sentence 1: words 8 and 4
Sentence 2: words 5 and 3
Sentence 3: words 1 and 6
Sentence 4: words 2 and 7
Sentence 5: words 1 and 3

Name ______________________________

toupee (275)	impromptu (277)	exultant (279)	scandal (282)
ultimately (282)	consequently (282)	indignantly (282)	

Directions: Write each vocabulary word on a piece of paper (one word per piece). Using the circle below, make a spinner. Now play the following game with a classmate. (It is a good idea to have a dictionary and thesaurus handy.) Place the papers in a small container. The first player draws a word from the container. The player then spins the spinner and follows the direction where the pointer lands. For example, if the player draws the word "scandal" and lands on "define," the player must define the word scandal. If the player's partner accepts the answer as correct, the first player scores one point and play passes to the second player. If the player's partner challenges the answer, the first player uses a dictionary or thesaurus to prove the answer is correct. If the player can prove the answer is correct, the player earns two points. If the player cannot prove the answer is correct, the opposing player earns two points. Play continues until all the words have been used. The player with the most points wins.

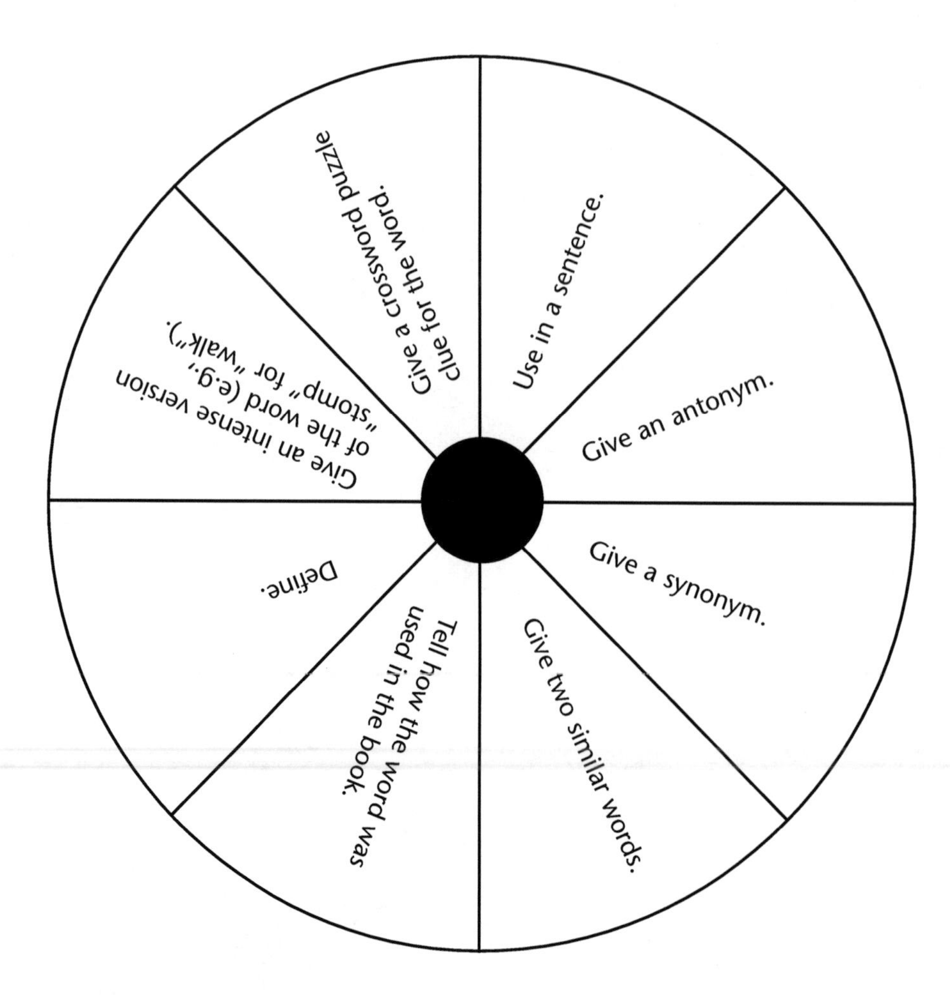

Name ______________________________ Activity #15 • Literary Analysis: Plot Development
Use During Reading

Story Map

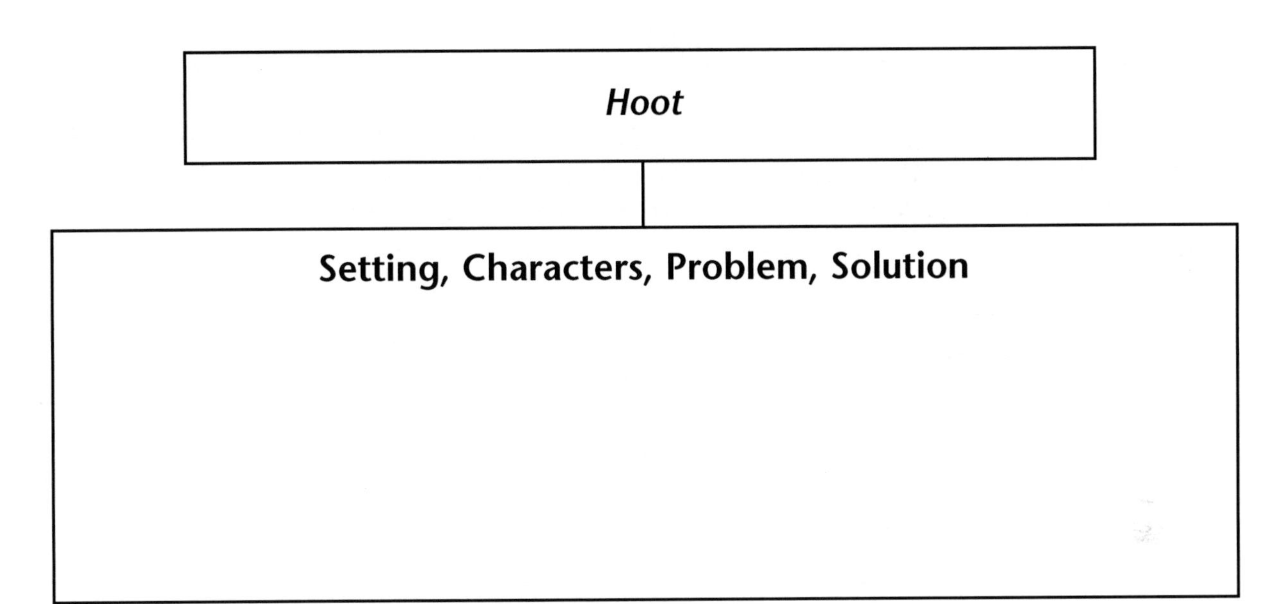

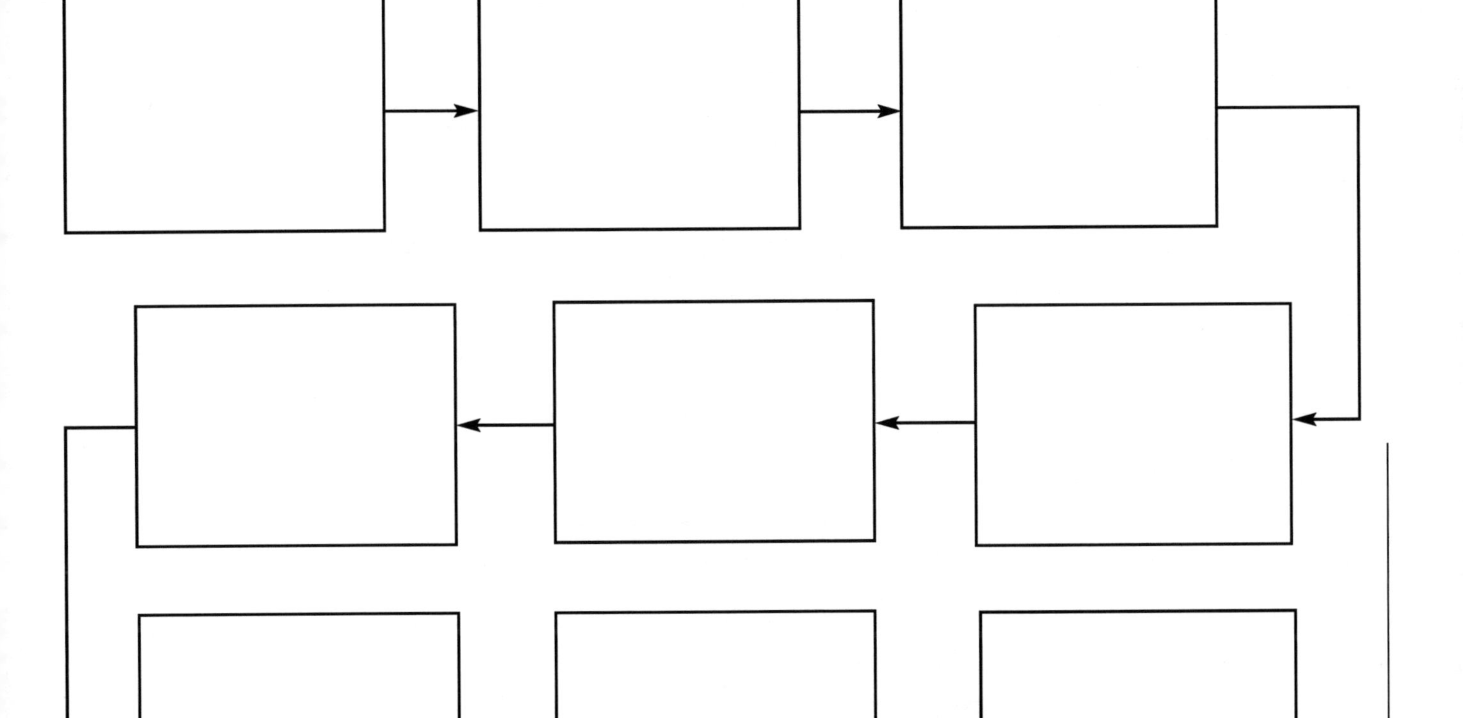

Name ________________________________

Foreshadowing Chart

Foreshadowing is the literary technique of giving clues to coming events in a story.

Directions: Think about *Hoot.* What examples of foreshadowing do you recall from the story? If necessary, skim through the chapters to find examples of foreshadowing. List at least four examples below. Explain what clues are given, then list the coming event that is suggested.

Foreshadowing	Page #	Clues	Coming Event

Name ______________________________

Conflict

The **conflict** of a story is the struggle between two people or two forces. There are three main types of conflict: person against person, person against nature or society, and person against himself/herself.

Directions: The characters in *Hoot* experience some conflicts in the story. In the space provided, list a conflict each character listed below experiences. Then explain how each conflict is resolved in the story.

Character: Roy

Conflict	Resolution

Character: Beatrice

Conflict	Resolution

Character: Mullet Fingers

Conflict	Resolution

Name ______________________________

Sociogram

Directions: Write the name of a different character in each circle. On the "spokes" surrounding each character's name, write several adjectives that describe that character. On the arrows joining one character to another, write a description of the relationship between the two characters. How does one character influence the other?

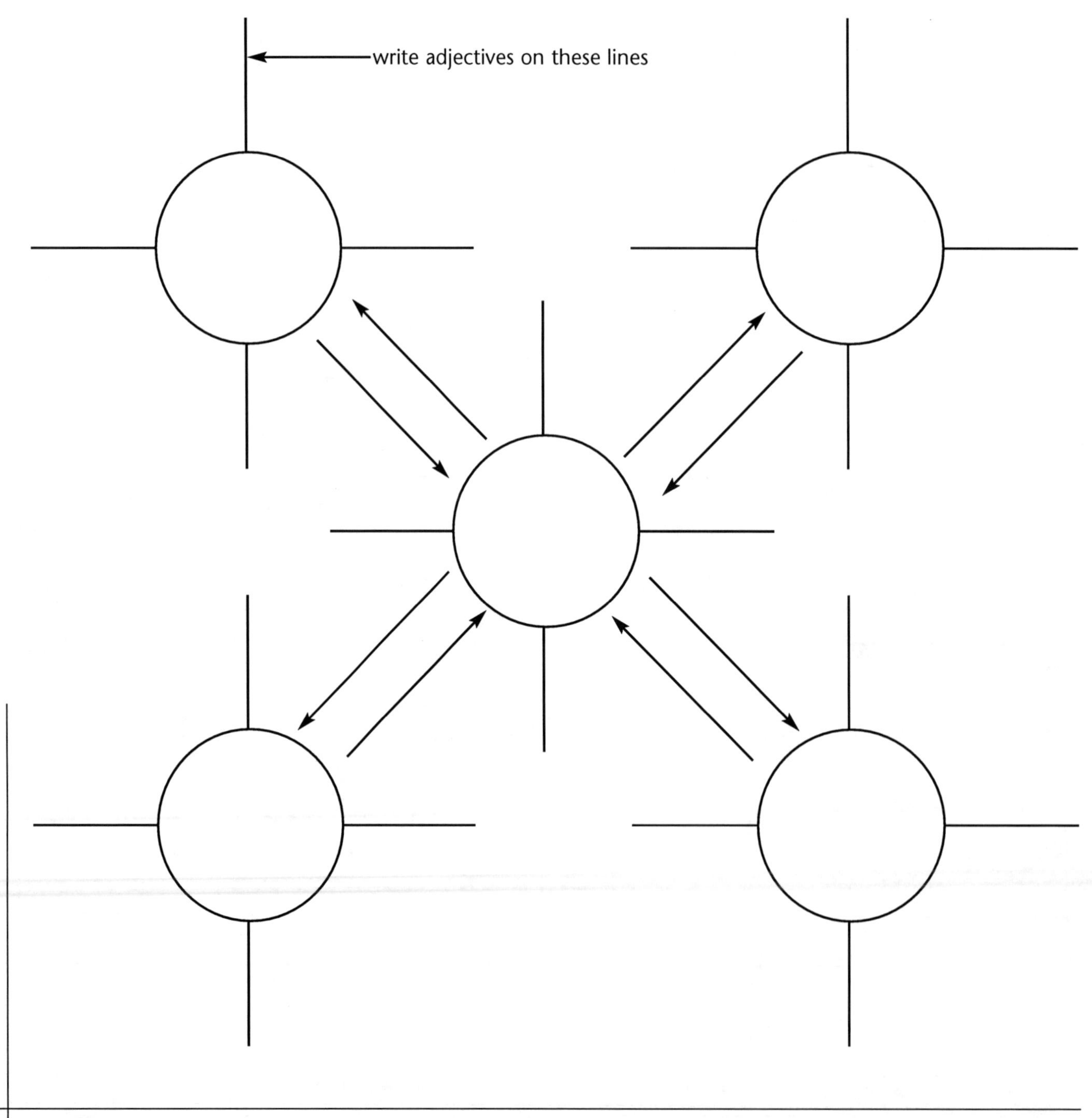

Name ______________________________

Character Chart

Directions: In the boxes across from each of the feelings, describe an incident or time in the book when each character experienced that feeling. You may use "not applicable" if you cannot find an example. In the last row, include a feeling you find important to the listed characters.

	Roy	**Dana**	**Officer Delinko**	**Curly**
Frustration				
Anger				
Fear				
Humiliation				
Relief				

Name ________________________________

Using Dialogue

Directions: Choose some dialogue from the book. Fill in the chart to evaluate the purpose of the dialogue and whether or not it is effective in moving the plot along.

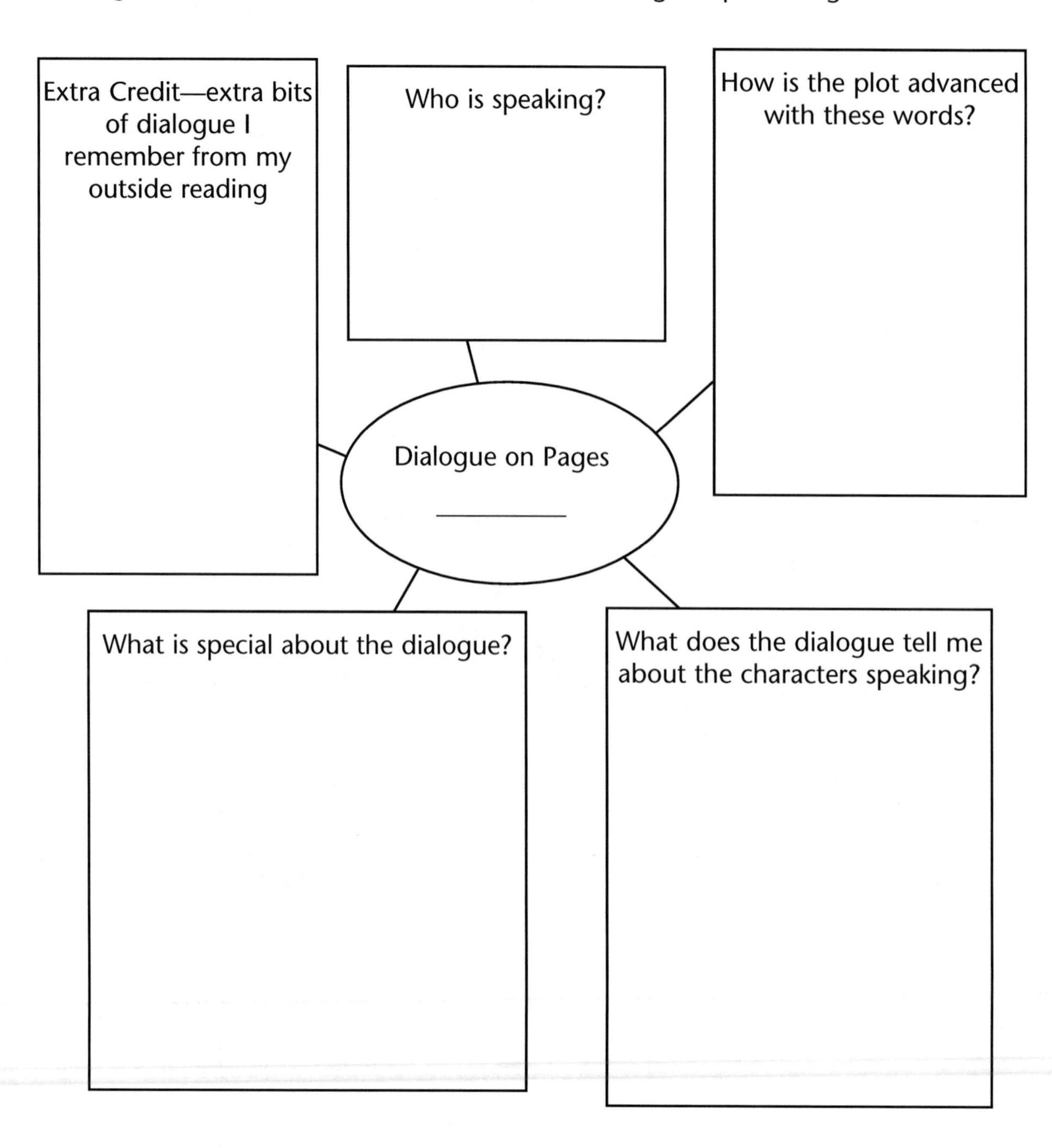

Name ______________________________

Making a Newspaper

Directions: Select one of the following topics. Research the topic by using books, the Internet, and other data sources in your library. Write a one-page article on your topic. Combine the articles to make a newspaper.

1. New restaurant to open
2. Escape from a Juvenile Detention Center
3. Nationalities in south Florida
4. Burrowing owls found on vacant lot
5. Debate on school uniforms
6. Airboat rides in the Everglades
7. Truancy
8. Truancy due to bullying
9. Home life
10. Poisonous snakes
11. Police procedures
12. Peaceful demonstrations
13. Endangered species saved

Name ______________________________

Matching: Match the following descriptions to the characters. Not all characters will be used.

____ 1. a new boy in school

____ 2. a bully

____ 3. a barefoot boy with a mission

____ 4. a police officer

____ 5. a federal employee

____ 6. a vice principal

____ 7. a fake fart champion

____ 8. a construction foreman

____ 9. a B-movie actress

____ 10. an executive for the pancake chain

a. Curly

b. Lonna

c. Kelly Colfax

d. Beatrice

e. Mr. Eberhardt

f. Chuck Muckle

g. Roy

h. Kimberly Lou Dixon

i. Dana

j. Garrett

k. Mullet Fingers

l. David Delinko

m. Mrs. Eberhardt

n. Miss Hennepin

Name ______________________________

True or False

___ 11. Dana wonders what will happen to the owls once bulldozing begins.

___ 12. Roy wants to move to Florida from Montana.

___ 13. A vandal punctures a truck's tires at the building site.

___ 14. Roy refuses to write an apology letter to Dana.

___ 15. Roy finds cottonmouth moccasins in the third sack at the campsite.

___ 16. Mullet Fingers lives in a panel truck in a car junkyard.

___ 17. Roy's bus suspension is lifted early.

___ 18. Garrett rescues Roy from the fight with Dana in the janitor's closet.

___ 19. German shepherds are guard dogs at the site.

___ 20. Two characters in *Hoot* use Roy's name instead of their own.

Name ______________________________

Directions: After each cause, list at least one effect.

Cause	**Effect**
1. Dana's first fight with Roy	______________________
2. police car windows painted black	______________________
3. Rottweilers at the construction site	______________________
4. Dana trying to steal cigarettes	______________________

True or False

___ 5. Dana writes an apology letter to Roy.

___ 6. Kimberly Lou Dixon quits her Mother Paula job.

___ 7. Garrett is expelled because of his fake farting routine.

___ 8. Beatrice bites the tire on Roy's motorcycle.

___ 9. Mullet Fingers escapes from juvenile detention.

___ 10. Roy catches a mullet with his hands.

Saving the Owls

Directions: Fill in the Venn Diagram below.

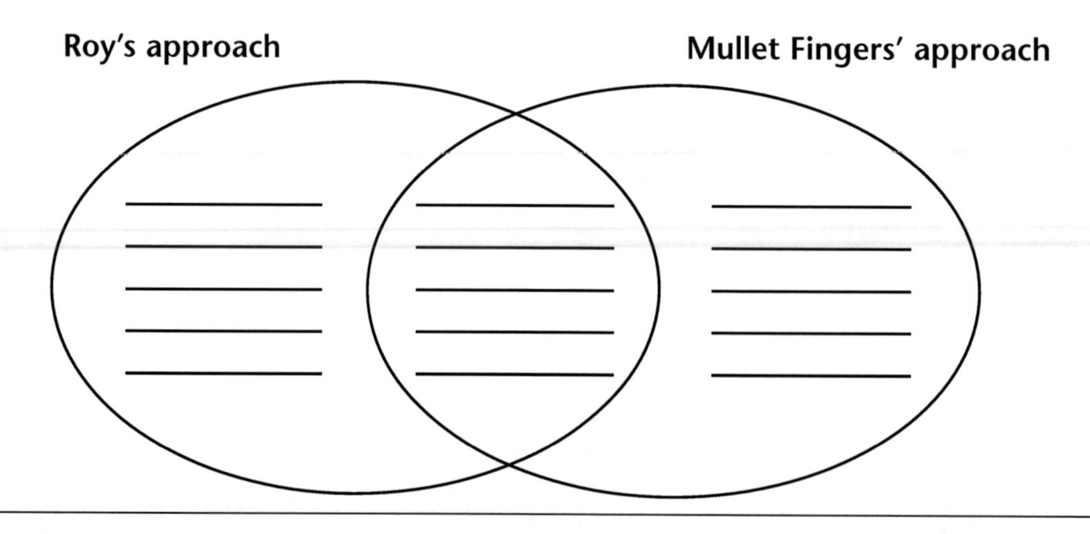

Name ______________________________

A. Multiple Choice: Select the best answer for each of the items below.

____ 1. Roy's approach to dealing with other students includes all of the following EXCEPT
(a) aggression
(b) mediation
(c) kindness
(d) listening

____ 2. Roy's feelings about moving from Montana could best be described as
(a) nonchalant
(b) angry
(c) delighted
(d) serene

____ 3. Mullet Fingers' mission concerns all of the following EXCEPT
(a) the environment
(b) protected species
(c) natural habitats
(d) capitalism

____ 4. Roy's relationship with his parents is best described as
(a) difficult
(b) abusive
(c) mean-spirited
(d) loving

____ 5. Vandalism at the site includes all of the following EXCEPT
(a) removing seats from earthmoving machines
(b) burning the job trailer
(c) putting snakes on the site
(d) painting car windows black

____ 6. Beatrice asks Roy for help because
(a) she doesn't want to be beaten up by Dana
(b) she needs money
(c) she has to cook dinner for her father
(d) her brother is injured

____ 7. To help save the owls, Roy does all of the following EXCEPT
(a) learn about the burrowing owls
(b) take digital pictures of the owls
(c) tell his class about the groundbreaking
(d) speak up at the groundbreaking

Name ______________________________

____ 8. Mullet Fingers' ability to catch a mullet with his bare hands is best described as
(a) routine
(b) mystical
(c) standard
(d) extraordinary

____ 9. All new construction in Florida requires a(n)
(a) groundbreaking ceremony
(b) franchise agreement
(c) environmental study
(d) bribe

____ 10. By the end of the story, Roy has found life in Florida as good as life in Montana because of all of the following EXCEPT
(a) new friends
(b) a solitary sanctuary at the *Molly Bell*
(c) the Everglades
(d) the weather

B. Identification: Identify each of the following and explain why each is important to the story.

11. owls
12. snakes
13. panel truck
14. portable bathrooms
15. pancakes
16. *Molly Bell*
17. apology letter
18. emergency room
19. survey stakes
20. Rottweilers

Name ______________________________

C. Essays

I. Analysis (Select A or B)

A. Write a composition of at least three paragraphs explaining how Roy deals with bullies and whether you agree or disagree with his method(s). Include specific examples from the book.

B. Mrs. Eberhardt tells Roy to make a decision about what is right or wrong by listening to what his heart and brain tell him. Write a composition of at least three paragraphs explaining how Roy applied this advice during a situation in the book. Then explain the decision you would have made in his place and why.

II. Critical/Creative Writing (Select A or B)

A. Write a letter to the editor of a newspaper defending the right of the owls to keep their breeding ground and an opposing letter supporting the right of the restaurant franchise to build. Include specific examples from the book in your letter.

B. Write a new ending to the story. Start with the current ending to the book, then jump in time to Roy's graduation from high school. Write a two-page description of what Beatrice, Dana, Garrett, Mullet Fingers, and Officer Delinko are doing now.

Answer Key

Activity #1: Dedication: For Carly, Ben, Samantha, Hannah, and, of course, Ryan; Title: Hoot; Cover Illustration: a blue cover with only the eyes and beak of an owl in the center; Teasers on the cover: On the inside front flap of the book jacket is a summary of Roy's problem. He's the new kid in a Florida town, and he misses Montana. Because a bully has his face mashed against the bus window, Roy sees a barefoot boy running from the bus and is intrigued. He senses a mystery and a list of characters and creatures he encounters is given; Friends' recommendations: Answers will vary; Reviewers' recommendations/awards won: Answers will vary but may include Publisher's Weekly calling the ending a sitcom type production which kids will like, School Library Journal's comment that the ecological values are a good science tie-in for school, and the Booklist review that states that kids will like to see adults making fools of themselves and will like the off-beat humor. The book is also a Newbery Honor book; Your predictions: Answers will vary.

Activity #2: 1. Idaho, Wyoming, South Dakota, North Dakota, and Canada 2. Atlantic Ocean and Gulf of Mexico 3. warm climate 4. Tallahassee 5.–6. Activity

Activity #3: Answers will vary.

Study Guide
Chapter One, pp. 1–12: 1. Trace Middle School 2. Dana Matherson 3. a barefoot boy 4. Mother Paula's All-American Pancake House 5. kids 6. an owl hole 7. the government 8. Garrett 9. go skateboarding at the mall 10. an outlaw

Chapter Two, pp. 13–23: 1. Louis from Haiti 2. punches him in the nose 3. He is hit by a golf ball. 4. Detroit 5. He cried in his room and then tried to run away. 6. It was the most beautiful place he had seen. 7. He can't ride the bus for two weeks, and he must write a letter of apology to Dana. 8. bruises made by Dana's fingers 9. mind his own business

Chapter Three, pp. 24–36: 1. Survey stakes were pulled up, and the holes were filled in. 2. He was scared. 3. Paramedics check him on the golf course, and the school nurse watches him at school. 4. United States Department of Justice 5. a cowboy riding a bull at a rodeo 6. arrangement 7. four feet 8. someone with a grudge against Mother Paula's pancake house 9. He wants to solve the mystery and receive a promotion.

Chapter Four, pp. 37–48: 1. at home; He'd called in sick. 2. Dana will beat him up. 3. Beatrice Leep 4. two burrowing owls 5. The windows are spray-painted black. 6. He's sorry for upsetting her, but whatever he did, it wasn't on purpose. 7. She squeezes her barbeque sandwich so hard it disintegrates. 8. to Dana's house 9. his apology letter

Chapter Five, pp. 49–57: 1. His injuries are his punishment, and they don't want to provoke his parents. 2. a campsite 3. blue and silver sparkles 4. He'd confronted grizzly bears in Montana. 5. A boy ties his wrists and puts a hood over his head. 6. Mullet Fingers 7. on the driving range of the golf course

Chapter Six, pp. 58–70: 1. the story of the black spray paint on the police car 2. It's across the street from Beatrice Leep's bus stop where he saw the running boy. 3. to cover an embarrassment to the police department 4. desk duty for a month and driving his police car only to work and back home 5. how many times Dana will beat up Roy 6. guard dogs 7. nothing; The campsite is gone. 8. Beatrice Leep

Chapter Seven, pp. 71–84: 1. to a car junkyard 2. Jo-Jo's Ice Cream and Sno-Cones 3. freshly baked peanut butter cookies. 4. He's her brother (actually a stepbrother). 5. from his police radio 6. He can catch little fish with his bare hands. 7. She bites it. 8. to call him if he hears any information about the job site and ask his dad to write a recommendation letter 9. He doesn't answer, but he takes off fast.

Chapter Eight, pp. 85–97: 1. The way it was bitten, it can't be repaired. 2. His mother calls the school about Dana not getting punished and says she wants justice. 3. Chuck Muckle, Mother Paula's vice president 4. put up a fence and bring in guard dogs 5. four Rottweilers 6. ospreys 7. It's swollen, probably from wrestling with his mother. 8. hit him 9. Beatrice

Chapter Nine, pp. 98–110: 1. Garrett 2. She had a miscarriage and lost a little baby girl. 3. Mr. Ryan, his American history teacher 4. He takes a shortcut through the gym and is the last one on the bus. 5. Snakes scare them. 6. to sue Mother Paula's 7. He twists it in an owl burrow. 8. through the window 9. none 10. the janitor's closet 11. Beatrice Leep

Chapter Ten, pp. 111–124: 1. strip him to his underpants and tie him to the flagpole 2. to his house 3. first aid supplies 4. a science experiment 5. hamburger 6. call juvenile authorities 7. Mullet Fingers 8. dog bite 9. to the construction site 10. Their mouths are taped shut. 11. feed the owls

Chapter Eleven, pp. 125–138: 1. a strip of green cloth 2. Mullet Fingers 3. He became dizzy and fell. 4. under a tree in a stranger's yard 5. a gun 6. the toilet seat 7. the bike Beatrice stole 8. write him a recommendation letter 9. the emergency room

Chapter Twelve, pp. 139–152: 1. They carry him upright between them. 2. so that Mullet Fingers' mother won't be notified 3. on the soccer field 4. The bites were not fresh and were infected. 5. to prepare supper for her dad 6. She had made a blood promise not to tell. 7. He hears a siren and doesn't want to see anything gory. 8. Officer Delinko 9. No one, it's empty. 10. that he doesn't know his name or where he is

Chapter Thirteen, pp. 153–162: 1. The Sibley Guide to Birds 2. about the snakes with their mouths taped shut 3. five owls in one tree 4. Give it some serious thought. 5. through a window in the women's restroom 6. the torn green shirt 7. what his heart tells Roy and what his brain tells him

Chapter Fourteen, pp. 163–179: 1. Garrett 2. to Beatrice's house 3. Her stepmother says she has to clean the house. 4. to Dana's house 5. to get money for doing Dana's homework 6. to talk things out and stop the fighting 7. to the junkyard to find Mullet Fingers 8. to the wreck of the *Molly Bell* 9. a mullet 10. He won't tell him, but says to be there.

Chapter Fifteen, pp. 180–196: 1. He moons him. 2. so Dana can catch him 3. He tells him where he can find a case of cigarettes. 4. His wife needed it, so she drops him off at the construction site. 5. He steps on two rattraps. 6. Roy Eberhardt 7. Officer Delinko 8. to the police station 9. a lawyer and a cigarette

Chapter Sixteen, pp. 197–210: 1. Garrett 2. He'll be locked up in juvenile hall. 3. his gun 4. The seats are missing on all the earthmoving equipment. 5. in one of the portable toilets 6. to the Everglades 7. nineteen 8. He understands that the wild places where animals live are in danger of being wiped out. 9. Beatrice whispering his name.

Chapter Seventeen, pp. 211–228: 1. on Wednesday, two days away 2. a robin or a wild chicken 3. broke three of his toes 4. She broke a tooth and was at the dentist. 5. no 6. twelve hours on/twelve hours off surveillance of the site 7. a fake alligator 8. October 9th 9. It's not with the others; maybe it's been checked out. 10. crickets for the owls 11. Curly

Chapter Eighteen, pp. 229–248: 1. because a reporter might see a police report and put the company's name in the papers 2. a baby owl 3. five or six inches 4. an ad for the groundbreaking ceremony 5. by biting a ring off her stepmother's toe 6. Mullet Fingers 7. because Mullet Fingers used his name at the hospital 8. his mother's digital camera 9. He talks about the protected owls and the site. 10. He'll get a note from home that says he can leave the school at noon to be at the site.

Chapter Nineteen, pp. 249–258: 1. his father 2. a napkin 3. the digital camera 4. Chuck E. Muckle and Kimberly Lou Dixon 5. crickets

Chapter Twenty, pp. 259–274: 1. students from Roy's history class and soccer teammates 2. Roy himself 3. the soccer team 4. a newspaper photographer and TV news 5. buried in a burrow with only his head poking out 6. rubber snakes 7. chops them with a shovel 8. Dig him up. 9. the actress playing Mother Paula 10. his mother

Chapter Twenty-one, pp. 275–281: 1. Napoleon Bridger Leep 2. story and pictures of the owl demonstration 3. tried to choke her 4. She is the reporter Chuck Muckle tried to choke. 5. An Environmental Impact Statement is missing, which makes it illegal to build.

Epilogue, pp. 282–292: 1. Councilman Grandy 2. Adam Sandler 3. cruise director 4. $50,000 5. because he is sluggish and sore-footed so he will be caught while Mullet Fingers escapes 6. to the wreck of the *Molly Bell*; tries to catch a mullet by hand, but can't 7. Mullet Fingers

Activity #4: 1. cackled 2. inedible 3. perpetually 4. doggedly 5. monetary 6. clammy 7. dispatcher 8. skeptical 9. consternation 10. unprovoked

Activities #5–#6: Answers will vary.

Activity #7: 1. defiant 2. noncommittal 3. squall 4. nonchalantly 5. ferociously 6. persistent 7. acknowledged 8. fervidly 9. oblivious 10. incentive 11. gala. 12. mulling—Antonyms to be circled: noncommittal, persistent, fervidly, oblivious, mulling

Activity #8: Answers will vary.

Activity #9: 1. avail 2. tandem 3. contemplate 4. skulking 5. fugitive 6. accusations 7. sullenly 8. subterranean Sentences will vary.

Activity #10: Answers will vary.

Activity #11: Nouns—fiasco, liberation, yarn, accomplice; Verbs—morphed, sabotaged, interjected; Adjectives—patronizing, florid, methodical, harrowing; Adverbs—malevolently, feverishly, wretchedly

Activity #12: 1. amber 2. incisor 3. gaunt 4. frenzied 5. jurisdiction 6. brawny 7. pilfered 8. tormentor 9. apprehended 10. allegations

Activities #13–#21: Answers will vary.

Comprehension Quiz #1: 1. g 2. i 3. k 4. l 5. e 6. n 7. j 8. a 9. h 10. f 11. T 12. F 13. F 14. F 15. T 16. T 17. T 18. F 19. F 20. T

Comprehension Quiz #2: 1.–4. Answers will vary. Possible answers: 1. Roy sees the barefoot boy. 2. Officer Delinko is put on desk duty. 3. Mullet Fingers is bitten. 4. Dana is sent to juvenile detention. 5. F 6. T 7. F 8. T 9. T 10. F Venn Diagram: Answers will vary.

Novel Test: (A) 1. a 2. b 3. d 4. d 5. b 6. d 7. b 8. d 9. c 10. d **(B)** Answers will vary. **(C)** Answers will vary.

